Mind-Bending
Cryptogram Puzzles

Editor: Colleen Collier
Puzzle Compilator: Sylvia Goulding
Additional Contributors: Peter Sorenti, Sue Curran
Page layout & Design: Linley Clode
Cover design: Gary Inwood Studios

Published by:
LAGOON BOOKS
PO BOX 311, KT2 5QW, UK
PO Box 990676, Boston, MA 02199, USA

www.lagoongames.com

ISBN 1-902813-49-9

© LAGOON BOOKS, 2001.

Lagoon Books is a trademark of
Lagoon Trading Company Limited.
All rights reserved.

Printed in Singapore.

Mind-Bending
Cryptogram Puzzles

LAGOON
BOOKS

INTRODUCTION

Full of ingenious codes and cryptic conundrums, this brain-twisting puzzle book presents the ultimate cranial challenge.

All the Mind-Bending puzzle books have been carefully compiled to give the reader a refreshingly wide range of challenges, some requiring only a small leap of perception, others deep and detailed thought. All the books share an eye-catching and distinctive style that presents each problem in an appealing and intriguing way. And this one guarantees hours of code-cracking fun! Either start at the beginning and work your way through all 80 puzzles, or else dip into it wherever and whenever you please.

But beware, cryptograms are highly addictive – you'll find this book hard to put down!

Food poisoning has incapacitated both the soprano and her understudy, and Kitty suddenly has to take over. Her computer printout of the libretto is garbled, but she glances at the last page and quickly discovers which opera is being performed. Which one is it?

Z1HH4KWQC 3J 5Z21H H2 X34...

J2 HT5H C21 P5C V2

5F5C Z4C2NX HT4 J45

TO: Zadie — New York
FROM: Bill — London

XFCMFTCBZ, 2ON,
BQQJUBKT GBKK,
AQJSJTG BJQXBZT,
IPGM E. LFMMFCZ
BJQOPQS

Bill from the London office sends an email to Zadie in the New York office to arrange a secret rendezvous. When and where will they meet?

TEMEH THLIS EAEIL
TGTMS EOAIO
1SFSOT 2WTSN

A Chinese visitor to America is having problems deciphering his travel instructions. Can you help him?

The voting intentions of Members of the Academy at the Oscars ceremony are strictly secret. One member's papers have been found but the message is encoded. Crack the code and find out who he is going to vote for in this year's 'Best Actor' category.

'"Last Tango in Paris" is showing at the Oscars retro slot. Mike will be staying at the Hotel Alpha again, like he did in November. Listen to 519 kHz Radio Sierra Nevada for hot news.'

What is the catty remark actor Bob Hope once made about Zsa Zsa Gabor?

Scene One - Take Three

KAG OMZ OMX OGX
MFQ LEM LEM SMN
AD'E MSQ NKF TQD
UZS EAZ TQD RUZ
SQD E.

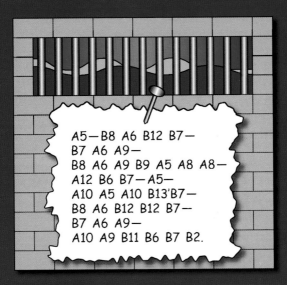

A prisoner has managed to escape from jail but first he left his confession on the warden's desk. Decipher the famous song lyrics to find out what crime he had committed.

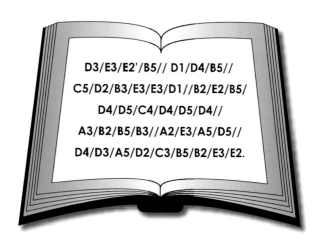

D3/E3/E2'/B5// D1/D4/B5//
C5/D2/B3/E3/E3/D1//B2/E2/B5/
D4/D5/C4/D4/D5/D4//
A3/B2/B5/B3//A2/E3/A5/D5//
D4/D3/A5/D2/C3/B5/B2/E3/E2.

As part of their exams, students at Cleverdale High School were asked to decipher this relevant maxim by Mark Twain. They were also told that the letters X and Y are represented by the same code. Can you do the same?

Luigi's gang plays in an orchestra during the daytime, but they are involved in crime at night. They are currently planning a major break-in. What are they after?

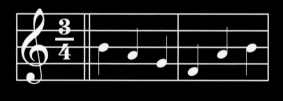

Pat receives a Valentine card with a coded message. Can you help her find out what it says and who sent it?

RVRT TWS RY

, RVRF SRY B LL' DN

, NM B SYWL LL'Y

, NTNLV GNLRD YM.

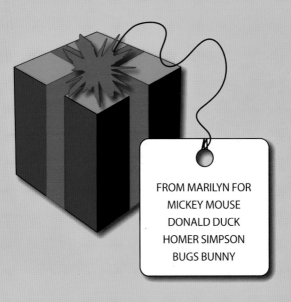

FROM MARILYN FOR
MICKEY MOUSE
DONALD DUCK
HOMER SIMPSON
BUGS BUNNY

John finds a present in front of his hotel door. He looks at the label and smiles because he realizes it's for him. How does he know that from the message above?

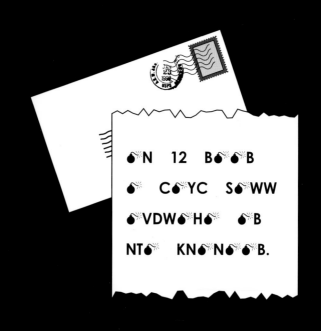

Police in the Thirteenth Precinct have received a coded letter. Do they need to take it seriously?

Two Martians have landed in California and interpreters are sent to try and communicate with them. The visitors hand them this piece of paper. What are they trying to say?

G	E	S	U	N	D
L	U	E	S	A	B
E	E	N	R	O	B
R	W	S	A	S	M
E	S	K	N	E	O
T	A	I	R	G	V

Smugglers are expecting a shipment of rum at midnight on a particular day in September. Can you tell them when they need to be ready?

2	14	13	1
10	5	4	11
4	8	12	6
14	3	1	12

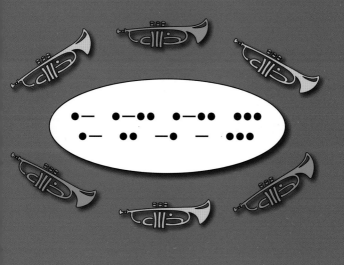

The New Orleans All Saints are playing the Chicago Red Bulls. In the stadium, all spectators have trumpets, and it is possible to hear a mixture of short and long blasts. Who has the greatest number of supporters in the audience?

The girls' high school has sent out invitations to their annual ball. To make things even more exciting, they have encoded their names and put them in a hat for each boy to pick one. Three friends – Dave, Jim, and Ron – have arrived together and picked their papers. Dave has '5204', Jim picked '1982', and Ron's paper reads '3482'. Who will be their dancing partners?

The highlight of this year's annual festival in Utopia is a travel competition. Eight town names have to be deciphered and the first letters of each town can then be rearranged to make up the name of a country. A trip for two to this place is the grand prize. Where are the winners going? (Some letters have already been given to help you).

When Jim Brown's galleon sank in the Caribbean four hundred years ago, he threw a bottle overboard with the following message. What does it say?

PEEDDY01EVACGIDS
1EM2ANAVAH.

Maria Angelhard Divinato
Oregon Nathan
Narnia Anunciata

An unclaimed suitcase was found in the luggage reclaim area. Attached to it was this label. How did Customs Officers know whom the case belonged to?

A B C D I E F G H I
I J K L I M N O P Q
R S T U V W X Y Z

'Mouth' Malone – so called because a rival gang cut out his tongue – lay on the sidewalk in a pool of blood. The cops have arrested three suspects at the scene of the crime – big, sweaty 'Red' O'Malley; bespectacled, computer whizz-kid 'Brains' Benson; and unpredictable 'Loose Canon' Collier. This is the message 'Mouth' left before he died. Who does it say killed him?

Scarface placed the following unusual job ads in a local paper. Crazy Bill studied these carefully and grinned because now he knew where the loot had been hidden. Where is it waiting to be discovered?

The Weekly Chronicle

SITUATIONS VACANT

Rain Driver
Muse Exterminator
State Manager
Sin Installer
Bus Diver
Judge of the Pace
Secret Gent

Paul showed George his latest painting. "Annie gave it to me," he said, "although she knows I don't like abstract art. She said, however, it's a musical message". George studied the picture for a while then shouted, "Oh wow! Don't you know? It's real nice – think of The Beatles".

WAWUWAW
IBIQIBI
TXTATXT
HAHYHAH
MNMOMNM

Rob and Helen want to see a controversial singer in concert without their parents realizing. They have hidden his name in this 'pattern'. Who do they want to see?

Three spies have ordered drinks in a bar, but they know that one of them has been poisoned. The barman slips them a coded message. Should they avoid the Margarita, the Cointreau or the Manhattan?

Mother could never remember her daughter Julie's telephone number (787326) but she always knew her other daughter Lisa's number was 129191. Why?

Tony's daughter has been on the phone to her boyfriend for hours and he has just overheard her last few words. He heard how she emphasized the words 'on Friday' and wondered whether there was more to her story than he could tell. Can you work out her secret plan?

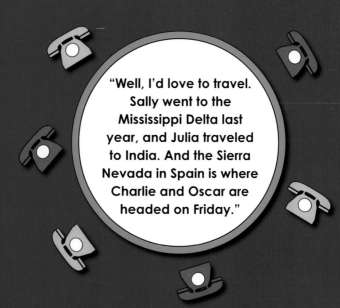

"Well, I'd love to travel. Sally went to the Mississippi Delta last year, and Julia traveled to India. And the Sierra Nevada in Spain is where Charlie and Oscar are headed on Friday."

When actress Barbara Stanwyck made the following cutting comment about Marilyn Monroe, was she talking about an anatomical curiosity or was she just jealous?

18 21 — 26 15 15 — 11 6 15 15 22 23
— 18 13 — 12 13 22 —
23 18 9 22 24 7 18 12 13, —7 19 22
— 4 12 9 15 23 — 4 12 6 15 23 —
16 22 22 15 — 12 5 22 9

Lorna is being interviewed for a new job. She noticed a poster with a lot of numbers behind the Human Resources Manager and he said, "That's the motto of our company. We all try to stick by it". What does the motto say?

At a party, guests have to catch a balloon and burst it. Inside are three words on pieces of paper and by adding the same letter to each word, three new words can be made. All the letters – one for each balloon – are the anagram of a popular male film star. Who is he?

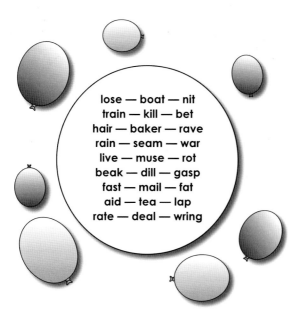

lose — boat — nit
train — kill — bet
hair — baker — rave
rain — seam — war
live — muse — rot
beak — dill — gasp
fast — mail — fat
aid — tea — lap
rate — deal — wring

Can you work out these famously witty words from the ever-funny Groucho Marx?

FUR TBG URE YBBXF SEBZ URE SNGURE. UR'F N CYNFGVP FHETRBA.

8...16 11 23 3...24 9 9 18
3 13...6 9 7...11 25 13...
26 8 12 12...17 9 25 3
12...9 25 5 9...5 16 3...
3 11 4 19 8 3 4...14 19 8
15 16 5...11 25 13...
8 25 5 9...11 13 17 11 22
3 25 5...4 9 9 26 12.

Marie is a Personal Assistant, and she knows all about her boss's messy private arrangements. For 'delicate' messages, they use a code. What is she trying to tell him this time?

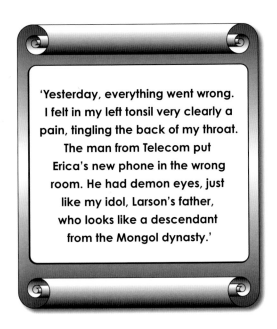

'Yesterday, everything went wrong.
I felt in my left tonsil very clearly a
pain, tingling the back of my throat.
The man from Telecom put
Erica's new phone in the wrong
room. He had demon eyes, just
like my idol, Larson's father,
who looks like a descendant
from the Mongol dynasty.'

Two thieves are preparing a list of items they are
hoping to steal when they break into a warehouse.
They are encoding the items so police cannot prove
anything if the list is discovered. What are they planning
to take?

The new chef prepares personalized meals for his guests. For which famous politician is he cooking this meal?

Melt some **butter** in a large saucepan. Add 1 **onion**, chopped, and 2 **garlic** cloves, crushed. Fry for a few minutes, then add 1/4 lb **ham**, cubed. Cook for 5 minutes. Add two handfuls of **rice**, and 1/4 bottle **white wine**. Add **salt** to taste. Simmer over a low heat, stirring occasionally. After ten minutes, add a handful of **uncooked shrimps**. In a frying pan, add 2 **eggs** and stir to scramble. Serve rice in a hot bowl with the egg on top, with a bowl of **grated cheese** and a salad of **endive**.

Mrs Marple gave her family a flowery riddle from beyond the grave when she encoded her will. Who will inherit her house and garden?

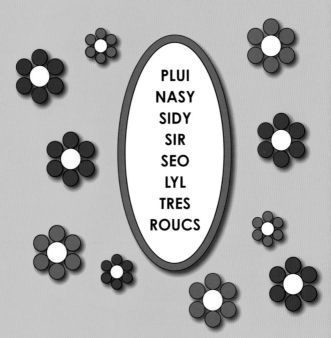

PLUI
NASY
SIDY
SIR
SEO
LYL
TRES
ROUCS

T
YA
HBK
IERE
MGCIA
EEHENN
METTMGD
TOIEYA NNTOC
TEUR RRO SS S.

Simon has left a secret message in Buffy's pigeonhole and has given her a clue, the word 'Egyptian'. What are they planning to do?

LIEWDO UNSIIN CTKTAD YHYHMS.

Mark is Radio Conundrum DJ. He announces the results of the 'Best Ever' song vote, and the first listener to decode the song title wins a bottle of champagne. What is it?

Mary-Jane Jenkins, Susan O'Sullivan and Barbara-Ann Petersen are standing outside the ice-cream parlor. Paul drives up to the girls, hooting. Who is he offering a ride to in his car?

toot — toot — toot
tooooot — tooooot — tooooot
toot — toot — toot

When she was planting spring bulbs in the garden, Jodie found an amulet covered with strange symbols. Her jeweler has valued it as priceless but what does the message on it say?

YHUFLQJHWRULA LV GIHHDWHG. JDXO LV QRZ ILUPOB LQ URPDQ KDQGV.

After several years of military success, Caesar sends a message to Rome ahead of his return. His message has been translated into English but what does it say?

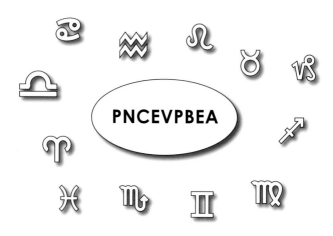

PNCEVPBEA

Sue visits a clairvoyant and asks about her future. In particular, she'd like to know about her future love life, but the clairvoyant can only indicate the star sign of her great love. What is it?

What is the following coded wisdom from George Bernard Shaw?

Joseph has given his Mother this Christmas wish list to pass to Santa Claus. What is he asking for this year?

CD
CC
CCCD
DDDDCDC
DCDCDCCCD
DDCDCDCC
DDCDCDCCC
CCDDDDDCDC
DCDCDCCCDDDCD
CDCDCCCCDDDDCCDD
CDCDCCCDDDCDCD
CDCDCDCD

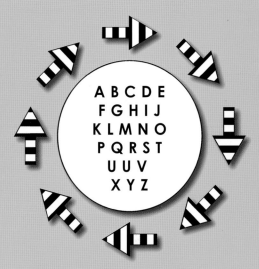

Jimmy is in prison because someone has grassed him up and run off with the money. He smuggles this note out of prison indicating the culprit, but was it Dwight, George, Carl or Willy?

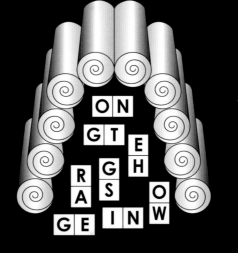

Duncan's history teacher has thought of a new way of keeping the interest of his students – each exam question is coded as a word puzzle. In this question, students have to work out how to fit the pieces of the puzzle together and then write something about this famous American once they know his/her name. Who is it?

Mike, Pete, and Trudie are propping up the bar. They've been here for hours, but it doesn't look like they'll be leaving soon! In fact, they've just decided to have another round of drinks. What did they order?

Pete leans over the counter and asks the barmaid, "Gal, can I have cool beer?"
Trudie decides on a 'rabid emu'.
Mike shakes his head pensively and asks, "Why ski?"

Madeleine knows exactly what kind of clothes she likes, and is telling Barry in no uncertain terms! However, as she doesn't want to be too blatant about it, she's encoded the name of her favorite designer. Can you rearrange the letters and put them in the colored grid to find out who it is?

T O E E
S V C A
A E N R
D A L L

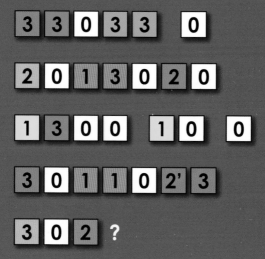

Mike is fond of art, poetry and math, and so he has rewritten the first line of a well-known Shakespearean sonnet in colorful numbers. What is it?

A gang is planning to break out of prison during a particular TV program. Which one have they decided on?

A cake shop has thought up a new ruse – they sell pieces of cake, each decorated with a letter. The first customer to combine eight pieces of cake into one round cake, so that the eight letters read correctly, will win a holiday. Where is the holiday to?

W hat is the name of this 'old man' whom nobody wants to get out of his bed?

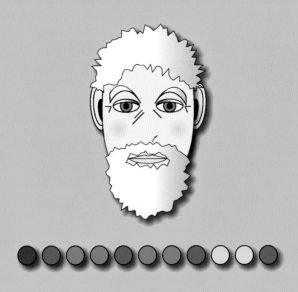

EQT JIGXQ BPKSGTZ FQJB

In order not to attract the attention of the FBI, two spies decide to pass on their secret files in a public place, while being watched by millions on television. Whose show have they decided to use?

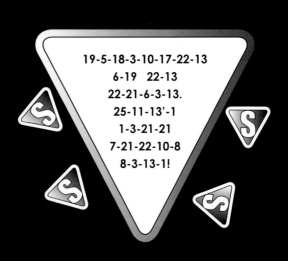

19-5-18-3-10-17-22-13
6-19   22-13
22-21-6-3-13.
25-11-13'-1
1-3-21-21
7-21-22-10-8
8-3-13-1!

L ois Lane has the hottest news on Superman. She has
quickly encoded her article so that no one can steal
her story. What does it say?

When Frank and Stella were married, she made a cross-stitch sampler for him. He has never yet been able to understand the jumble of letters on it though. Can you help decipher it?

James opens his email and finds an anonymous message with a garbled subject matter. What should he do?

TO: James
FROM: ?

EPHL HL K
WHDGL – MI
YIE IJCY.

Every time Liam visits the library, he chooses Locker number 129113 for his bags. Why?

JEIOASADNTG
BNZWAALPVEPO
NANAYOPIRODIUT
BASGFCINDLUL
HIFATTNXMIAY
GKKGCHIRESR
JUEBCNSNOY
UCHLRASTUFH
DNISAIRVOUT
SDINEA

Sailor Jim has a string of letters tattooed all over his back that contain the names of all his 'brides'. He has hidden them in order not to upset any future girlfriends. Can you find them?

A briefcase full of secret documents has been depo... in one of the St Louis Airport lockers, and Agen... has to advise Agent Z of the locker number. This is th... message he cables. What does it mean?

Houston 67 miles

New Orleans 96 miles

Memphis 68 miles

Dallas 58 miles

Dan's computer games console has a secret entry code. You can only start playing once you have found the password. Below is his personal *aide memoir*. Can you work out what his personal password is?

	YES	NO
1	BEER	RUM
2	BREAD	BUTTER
3	RADIO	TV
4	BATH	SOAP
5	HOTEL	MOTEL
6	QUESTION	ANSWER
7	BUDDY	FRIEND
8	YARD	HOUSE
9	CAKE	TART
10	DANCE	SONG

Sage = 32, Chives = 66
Mint = 56, Meet me in Basil.

After an evening's flirtation in the hotel bar, Josh cheekily asks Christa for her room number. But Christa doesn't want to make it too easy for him so she gives him this riddle. What room is she in?

These domino pieces can be fitted together to give the names of a couple that often hit the headlines. Who are they?

Which famous Commander of the 'Starship Enterprise' is hidden in the codes devised by Quark, the Ferengi barkeeper, below? Only one of the codes is correct for each letter.

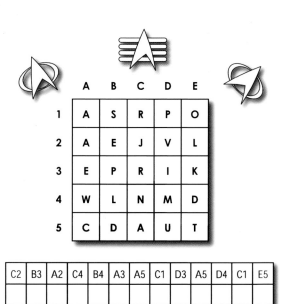

C2	B3	A2	C4	B4	A3	A5	C1	D3	A5	D4	C1	E5

A5	B2	A1	E5	D2	D5	B1	D1	C5	B1	A2	A4	E4

W hat is the important text message that Meg has
tapped into her mobile phone?

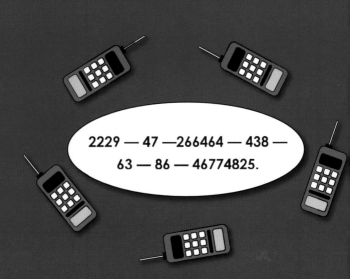

2229 — 47 —266464 — 438 —
63 — 86 — 46774825.

Mike has problems remembering his Personal Identification numbers, so he has changed them all to 6453. Why? The number has nothing to do with any dates in his life!

WGEK JDAK
YVEOA TV
WDJG

Two thieves are planning to break into the Louvre to steal some major works of art. This code reveals what they are hoping to take. Can you work it out?

The CIA know there is a spy in Congress. The head of the CIA suspects a younger ●●●●●●● from one of the eastern states of ●●●●●●●. The two missing words are anagrams of each other. What are they?

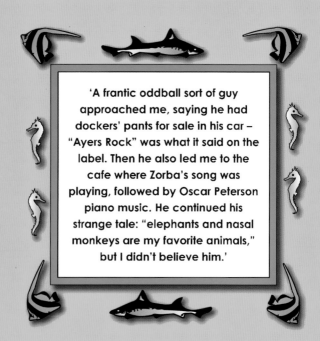

Hidden in the following story are the names of eight types of fish. Can you find them all?

'A frantic oddball sort of guy approached me, saying he had dockers' pants for sale in his car – "Ayers Rock" was what it said on the label. Then he also led me to the cafe where Zorba's song was playing, followed by Oscar Peterson piano music. He continued his strange tale: "elephants and nasal monkeys are my favorite animals," but I didn't believe him.'

BOⅠⅠEBC-EIƐI

When Jerry came home, the whole house had been turned upside down. At first he thought he'd been burgled, but then he noticed the strange scribbles shown in the dust on the windowsill. What had happened?

Grieg – 'Peer Gynt Suite'
Gershwin – 'Rhapsody in Blue'
Holst – 'The Planet Suite'
Ravel – 'Bolero'

Michael is a secret agent. As soon as a particular piece of music starts, another agent will go to the bathroom and leave a box of cigarettes with a message. At the end of the piece, Michael must go and get it. The only clue he has is the message, "My very esteemed Mr Johnson: show understanding! No problems!" Which piece of music from the above concert program is he waiting for?

What is the feminist message hidden here?

A — 18 D 10 A 11 —
18 C 16 6 D E 16 — A — 10 A 11
— C 15 — 9 C 8 B — A —
4 C 15 6 — 18 C 16 6 D E 16 —
A — I C 2 20 2 9 B.

Nathalie tells her friend about the latest developments in her love life. She doesn't want anyone else to understand as they might give her secret away, so she encodes her story. Who does she love and whom is she finished with?

"I'm bored with Boxing Day, but I'm really enjoying 17th March."

WE CPE CJJ GN
THE ISTTEP, BST
UMOE MD SU CPE
JMMKGNI CT THE
UTCPU.

What is this famous saying by Oscar Wilde?

Agents are comparing prices in rival stores and messaging their head office for price control. This is how the messages were sent and received but what does it all mean?

– MEMO –

267638427 836
7372368 2432737.
374657 6673 397367483.

– MEMO –

6333 6673 338245.

Sophia has had so many facelifts, it is impossible to guess her age. Even her doctor has forgotten so she has revealed the truth to him through this grid. How old is she really?

13	4	10	16	22
24	15	1	7	18
6	17	23	14	5
20	21	12	3	9
2	8	19	25	11

The results of the end-of-year exams are clear but they haven't yet been made public. The head of the school informs the teachers which students have passed by posting this coded message on the staff-room noticeboard. Can you work out their names?

'All the pets will go to children's homes. The most vicious animal is a rodent, but even gerbil Louis can't stay here. For the girls we have rabbits, but some are going to the beach – risky for tortoises. The sand rather gets under their shells. Last year, we had an awfully cute tarantula, but the noise of the banjo excited her and she always hid under the carpet Ellie likes playing on.'

LIBUN BIGDRUNH BURNCNKS
LOS YTPG SEULAMER BATSLUN
MEO MADRESTM TEROMATD
WATAT CIE

It looks like the train robbers have succeeded, but the police are after them and they don't want to take any chances. So they decide to flee the country and Mervyn asks Dale to organize the tickets. From this code, can you work out where they are headed?

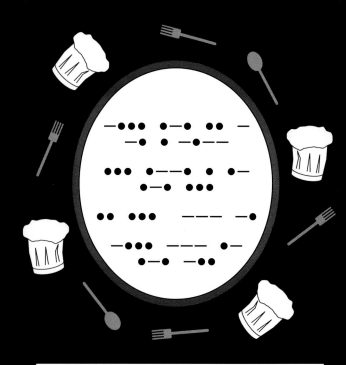

Bob, the trainee ship's cook, was very excited when he recognized a singing star on his cruise ship, and so he immediately sent this message to his brother. Who has he seen?

Monkey Dog, a state-of-the-art spaceship, is traveling through time. The crew have landed on a strange planet and asked their on-board computer where they are and what year they have landed in. Unfortunately, the computer gets its messages all garbled up and produces the following. What does it mean?

Kim is a music teacher having problems at home. She confides the problems to her Mother by humming a message to her over the phone. Can you work out what has happened?

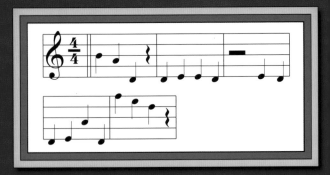

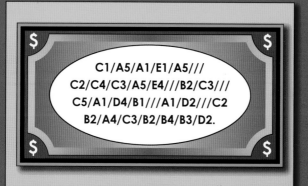

C1/A5/A1/E1/A5///
C2/C4/C3/A5/E4///B2/C3///
C5/A1/D4/B1///A1/D2///C2
B2/A4/C3/B2/B4/B3/D2.

Kidnappers are holding a millionaire's daughter. They have sent a ransom note, which her father and the police are desperately trying to unscramble. What does it say?

ZOO

16/A/11/17/8/2
17/C/5/D 12/D
21/E/11/E/11/E/7.

George the gorilla has learned to communicate with the help of a simple coding machine. What is he trying to tell the zookeeper?

Judy and Marion have decided to encrypt their emails so that they can gossip safely and undetected about any member of staff. Here's their most recent exchange of messages. Can you decipher them and find out what they are saying?

TO: Judy
FROM: Marion

185 is 563! RU4
19h0 97 56789?

TO: Marion
FROM: Judy

8'5 4 14745y.

TO: Judy
FROM: Marion

37465 90!

Page 6

The numbers 5 to 1 replace all vowels, and the consonants are used in reverse order.

'**Butterfly is about to die...
so that you may go
away beyond the sea...**'
The Opera is 'Madam Butterfly'.

Page 7

Two letters at a time are transposed.

'**Wednesday, 2pm, Arrivals Hall,
British Airways, John F Kennedy
Airport**'

Page 8

Write the message vertically in 6 rows (rather than 5), then read it horizontally across.

'**The motel is 12 miles west of the gas station**'

Page 9

The name is hidden using NATO's phonetic spelling alphabet – '**T**ango **O**scar **M**ike **H**otel **A**lpha **N**ovember **K**ilo (Hertz) **S**ierra'. Therefore the name of the winning actor is **Tom Hanks**.

Page 10

Alpha and Omega – The alphabet has 'moved along', with the code letter A starting underneath the message letter O. In addition, the message is broken up into three-letter chunks.

"**You can calculate Zsa Zsa Gabor's age by the rings on her fingers.**"

Page 11

The first thirteen letters of the alphabet are coded as A, the second thirteen as B. Within each group they are numbered backwards.

A	B	C	D	E	F	G	H	I	J	K	L	M
A	A	A	A	A	A	A	A	A	A	A	A	A
13	12	11	10	9	8	7	6	5	4	3	2	1

N	O	P	Q	R	S	T	U	V	W	X	Y	Z
B	B	B	B	B	B	B	B	B	B	B	B	B
13	12	11	10	9	8	7	6	5	4	3	2	1

'**I shot the sheriff but I didn't shoot the deputy**' (Eric Clapton)

Page 12

The letter A stands in the middle, and the other letters are 'wound' around it clockwise in a spiral shape. Each letter is represented by its grid position, as indicated by letter plus number.

"Don't let school interfere with your education."

Page 13
Using the names of the musical notes shown, the message is revealed to be '**Bag Fabage (FABERGE) Egg**'.

Page 14
All the vowels have been omitted and the sequence of consonants reversed, to read, '**My darling Valentine, you'll always be mine, and I'll be yours forever, your sweet Trevor**'.

Page 15
The names contain the letter U four times. 4 x U = fo(u)r you

Page 16
All the vowels are replaced by a bomb, the consonants are moved forward from their original position first by one, then two, then three etc. positions (not counting the vowels), starting from the letter X.

Therefore the message reads, '**At 12 noon a bomb will explode in the station**'.

Page 17
Start in the top left corner and move only one field at a time, in any direction, including diagonally. Every field can be visited only once. The message reads, '**Guns and bombs are useless. We're taking over**'.

Page 18
All columns and rows add up to 30, so the rum is due to arrive on the 30th September.

Page 19
The system used is Morse Code.

A = • —
I = • •
L = • — • •
N = — •
S = • • •
T = —

Therefore they are All Saints supporters.

Page 20
The three names of the boys form the following code.

Therefore Dave will dance with Jane, Jim with Dora, and Ron with Vera.

Page 21

A	B	C	D	E	F	G	H	I	J	K	L	M
♥	✿	✤	♦	✕	✿	✿	☛	➤	➤	✳	●	○

N	O	P	Q	R	S	T	U	V	W	X	Y	Z
■	★	✰	I	◻	▲	▼	◆	◆	◖	❰	❮	✔

Paris — Ottawa — Rome — Toronto — Utopia — Geneva — Athens — Los Angeles. The trip for two is to **Portugal**.

Page 22
Read the message backwards to get, '**(From) Havana, (go) 2 m(iles) E(ast), 1 m(ile) S(outh) dig (in) cave 10 yd(s) deep**'.

Page 23
The first letter of each word is used to spell the owner's name – **Madonna**.

Page 24
The letter **I** is included four times – **four Is = four-eyes**. Therefore, bespectacled 'Brains' Benson is revealed as the murderer.

Page 25
There is either a consonant or a vowel

missing in each of the job titles. Together they reveal the hiding place.

M**O**use Exterminator

Secret **A**Gent

Sin**K** Installer

TRain Driver

Bus D**R**iver

Judge of the P**E**ace

EState Manager

The loot is buried under the **Oak Tree**.

Page 26

Each color and symbol stands for a letter…

Scarlet = S

🍁 = H

● = E

💡 = L

Orange = O

Violet = V

E = E

Scarlet = S

Yellow = Y

Orange = O

U = U

The message is the Beatles song, '**She Loves You**'.

Page 27

MNM = Eminem

Page 28

The letters are half-covered and mirrored across the word. Hiding the bottom half of the word makes it easier to guess which letters they are and reveals that the 'Manhattan' is poisoned.

Page 29

L = 12; **I** = 9; **S** = 19; and **A** = 1, which

converts to **129191**.

Page 30

Tony's daughter is using the NATO spelling alphabet and is telling her boyfriend that she will meet him 'on Friday' at the **D**elta **I**ndia **S**ierra **C**harlie **O**scar (**Disco**).

Page 31

After the first 13 letters, the alphabet 'returns' on itself, so that the last letter (Z) ends up under the first one (A). To decode the message, take the letter above or below the code letter respectively.

A	B	C	D	E	F	G	H	I	J	K	L	M
Z	Y	X	W	V	U	T	S	R	Q	P	O	N

"**Her body has gone to her head.**"

Page 32

The alphabet is replicated in reverse order by the numbers 1 to 26.

A	B	C	D	E	F	G	H	I	J	K	L	M
26	25	24	23	22	21	20	19	18	17	16	15	14

N	O	P	Q	R	S	T	U	V	W	X	Y	Z
13	12	11	10	9	8	7	6	5	4	3	2	1

So the motto reads, '**If all pulled in one direction, the world would keel over**'.

Page 33

lo**U**se — **U**-boat — **U**nit

Strain — **S**kill — be**S**t

Chair — ba**C**ker — **C**rave

Train — s**T**eam — war**T**

Olive — m**O**use — ro**O**t

b**R**eak — d**R**ill — g**R**asp

f**E**ast — **E**-mail — f**E**at

Maid — tea**M** — la**M**p

I**r**ate — **I**deal — w**I**ring

The answer is **Tom Cruise**.

Page 34

A	B	C	D	E	F	G	H	I	J	K	L	M
N	O	P	Q	R	S	T	U	V	W	X	Y	Z

N	O	P	Q	R	S	T	U	V	W	X	Y	Z
A	B	C	D	E	F	G	H	I	J	K	L	M

"**She got her good looks from her father. He's a plastic surgeon.**"

Page 35

The letters are encoded numerically, following the typical 'QWERTY' keyboard.

Q	W	E	R	T	Y	U	I	O	P
1	2	3	4	5	6	7	8	9	10

A	S	D	F	G	H	J	K	L
11	12	13	14	15	16	17	18	19

Z	X	C	V	B	N	M
20	21	22	23	24	25	26

"**I have booked you and Miss Jones onto the earlier flight and into adjacent rooms.**"

Page 36

The items 'straddle' one or two words in the text.

'Yesterday, everything went wrong. I felt in my left ton**SIL VER**y clearly a **PAIN, TING**ling the back of my throat. The man from Tele**COM PUT ER**ica's new phone in the wrong room. He had de**MON EY**es, just like my i**DOL**, **LARS**on's father, who looks like a descendant from the Mon**GOL D**ynasty.'

Page 37

B – utter
O – nion
G – arlic
H – am
R – ice
W – hite wine
S – alt
U – ncooked shrimps

E – ggs
G – rated cheese
E – ndive
The first letters of all the ingredients, rearranged, spell **George W Bush**.

Page 38

Each word has one letter missing. Rearranged, the missing letters make up the name of the recipient.

T – ulip
P – ansy
D – **A** – isy
I – ris
R – ose
L – **I** – ly
A – ster
C – rocus
Therefore the heir is **Patricia**.

Page 39

The message is written in a pyramid shape (Egyptian) from left to right, and then read down each column.

'**Meet me tonight in the cemetry. Bring your stake and a cross**'

They are planning to slay vampires.

Page 40

Mark has used a simple columnar transposition.

L	U	C	Y
I	N	T	H
E	S	K	Y
W	I	T	H
D	I	A	M
O	N	D	S

The answer is '**Lucy in the Sky with Diamonds**' by The Beatles.

Page 41

It is Morse Code for **SOS**, which are Susan O'Sullivan's initials.

Page 42

T U T A N K H A M E N

The amulet belonged to Egyptian King, **Tutankhamen**.

Page 43

"**Vercingetorix is defeated. Gaul is now firmly in Roman hands.**"

Page 44

The alphabet is written in two halves, the second half continuing under the first half, in the same direction.

A	B	C	D	E	F	G	H	I	J	K	L	M
N	O	P	Q	R	S	T	U	V	W	X	Y	Z

The great love in Sue's life will be a **Capricorn**.

Page 45

"**Truth is the one thing nobody**

will believe."

Page 46

Joseph wants lots and lots of CDs!

Page 47

There are two **U**s in his note – a **double U** – therefore **W**illy has the money.

Page 48

George Washington.

Page 49

The orders are anagrams. Pete has ordered 'an alcoholic beverage', Trudie a 'Drambuie', and Mike a 'whisky'.

Page 50

The designer is **Donatella Versace**.

Page 51

All the vowels are white 0s, the remaining consonants are divided into color-coded groups of three and numbered 1 – 2 – 3.

"**Shall I compare thee to a summer's day?**"

Page 52

SDJFTE**V**RKUOP**R**BYDD**PS**POP**K**RNIXZNK GGE**P**OIJN**R**SXGGS7HT**H**NMBOZWQ**WR**.

All the letters appear in the right

sequence and the answer is '**The Jerry Springer Show**'.

Page 53

Tasmania.

Page 54

M = ●
I = ●
S = ●
P = ●

Mississippi ('ol' man river').

Page 55

The letters read in the opposite direction, and they are also moved three letters along.

A	B	C	D	E	F	G	H	I	J	K	L	M
X	W	V	U	Y	S	R	Q	P	O	N	M	L

N	O	P	Q	R	S	T	U	V	W	X	Y	Z
K	J	I	H	G	F	E	D	C	B	A	Z	Y

So the answer is '**The Oprah Winfrey Show**'.

Page 56

Lois used an old-fashioned printers' phrase as a base for her code, 'The quick brown fox jumps over the lazy dog'.

T	H	E	Q	U	I	C	K	B	R	O	W	N
1	2	3	4	5	6	7	8	9	10	11	12	13

F	O	X	J	U	M	P	S	O	V	E	R
14	11	15	16	5	17	18	19	11	20	3	10

T	H	E	L	A	Z	Y	D	O	G
1	2	3	21	22	23	24	25	11	26

"**Superman is an alien. Don't tell Clark Kent**"

Page 57

Every second letter reads as two words and the in-between letters are a date in Roman numerals.

Y	O	U	R	S	F	O	R	E	V	E	R
M	C	M	L	X	X	X	V	I	I	I

So the sampler reads, '**Yours forever, 1988**'.

Page 58

The message was encrypted using the 'QWERTY' keyboard sequence, and replaced with the alphabetical sequence of letters.

Q	W	E	R	T	Y	U	I	O	P
A	B	C	D	E	F	G	H	I	J

A	S	D	F	G	H	J	K	L
K	L	M	N	O	P	Q	R	S

Z	X	C	V	B	N	M
T	U	V	W	X	Y	Z

The message reads, '**This is a virus – do not open**'.

Page 59

A	B	C	D	E	F	G	H	I	J	K	L	M
1	2	3	4	5	6	7	8	9	10	11	12	13

N	O	P	Q	R	S	T	U	V	W	X	Y	Z
14	15	16	17	18	19	20	21	22	23	24	25	26

His name reads as '**12 – 9 – 1 – 13**'.

Page 60

He's had one or more extra letters added between the letters that make up his girlfriends' names, to make these more difficult to discover.

JEIOASADNTGBNZWAALPVEPONANAY
OPIRODIUTBASGFCINDLULHIFATTNXMI
AYGKKGCHIRESRJUEBCNSNOYUCHLRA
STUFHDNISAIRVOUTSDINEA

Joanna, Penny, Rita, Gillian, Maggie, Jenny, Claudia, Rosie.

Page 61

All consonants count as 10, all vowels as 9 miles. Therefore St Louis would be 40 + 27 = 67 miles, so the documents are hidden in locker number **67**.

Page 62

The letters that make up his ten-letter

password are found in the words in the 'Yes' column, but not in the words in the 'No' column.

YES

B**E**ER
B**R**EAD
RADIO
B**A**TH
HOTEL
QUESTION
B**U**DDY
YA**R**D
C**A**KE
DANC**E**

The password is '**Earthquake**'.

Page 63

Christa added all the positional values of the letters in the alphabet together.

A	B	C	D	E	F	G	H	I	J	K	L	M
1	2	3	4	5	6	7	8	9	10	11	12	13

N	O	P	Q	R	S	T	U	V	W	X	Y	Z
14	15	16	17	18	19	20	21	22	23	24	25	26

Basil is 2 + 1 + 19 + 9 + 12 = 43, so Christa is waiting in room number **43**.

Page 64

Bill and Hilary Clinton.

Page 65

Jean-Luc Picard.

Page 66

The mobile phone keys are arranged as follows.

2	3	4	5
Abc	def	ghi	jkl

6	7	8	9
mno	pqrs	tuv	wxyz

Meg's message reads, '**Baby is coming. Get me to hospital**'.

Page 67

He has used the numbers relating to his name on a mobile phone keypad.

2	3	4	5
Abc	def	ghi	jkl

6	7	8	9
mno	pqrs	tuv	wxyz

M = 6, I = 4, K = 5, E = 3.

Page 68

He has used a typographer's sentence as an encoding grid – 'Sphinx of black quartz judge my vow'.

S	P	H	I	N	X	O	F	B	L	A	C	K
A	B	C	D	E	F	G	H	I	J	K	L	M

Q	U	A	R	T	Z	J	U	D	G	E
N	O	K	P	Q	R	S	O	T	U	V

M	Y	V	O	W
W	X	Y	G	Z

'**Mona Lisa**' and '**Venus de Milo**'.

Page 69

Senator – treason.

Page 70

'A franti**C OD**dball sort of guy approached me, saying he **HAD DOCK**ers' pants for sale in his ca**R** – "**AY**ers Rock" was what it said on the label. Then he al**SO LE**d me to the cafe where Zor**BA'S S**ong was playing, followed by Os**CAR P**eterson piano music. He continued his strange tal**E**: "**EL**ephants and na**SAL MON**keys are my favorite animals," but I didn't believe him.'

Page 71

The bottom half of the message is covered up and repeated in mirror writing. It was a **Poltergeist**.

Page 72

The initials of the words in the message read **M – V – E – M – J – S – U – N – P**, which are the same as the sequence of planets starting from the Sun (**M**ars – **V**enus – **E**arth – **M**ercury – **J**upiter – **S**aturn – **U**ranus – **N**eptune – **P**luto). He is therefore being instructed to wait for Holst's '**The Planet Suite**'.

Page 73

The vowels are encoded as A–E, the consonants as 1–21.

A	B	C	D	E	F	G	H	I	J	K	L	M
A	1	2	3	B	4	5	6	C	7	8	9	10

N	O	P	Q	R	S	T	U	V	W	X	Y	Z
11	D	12	13	14	15	16	E	17	18	19	20	21

'**A woman without a man is like a fish without a bicycle.**'

Page 74

Boxing Day, 26th December, is St Stephen's Day and 17th March is St Patrick's Day, so she is bored with Stephen and in love with Patrick.

Page 75

Every group of three letters is reversed, so ABC becomes CBA, etc.

A	B	C	D	E	F	G	H	I	J	K	L	M
C	B	A	F	E	D	I	H	G	L	K	J	O

N	O	P	Q	R	S	T	U	V	W	X	Y	Z
N	M	R	Q	P	U	T	S	X	W	V	Z	Y

"**We are all in the gutter, but some of us are looking at the stars**".

Page 76

The mobile phone keys are arranged as follows.

2	3	4	5
Abc	def	ghi	jkl

6	7	8	9
mno	pqrs	tuv	wxyz

'**Cosmetics ten percent cheaper. Drinks more expensive.**' '**Need more detail.**'

Page 77

All columns and rows add up to 65, indicating that Sophia is 65 years old.

Page 78

'All the pets will go to children's homes. The most vicious anima**L IS A** rodent, but even ger**BIL L**ouis can't stay here. For the girls we ha**VE RA**bbits, but some are going to the bea**CH – RIS**ky for tortoises. The **SAND RA**ther gets under their shells. Last year, we ha**D AN** awfully cute tarantula, but the noise of the ban**JO E**xcited her and she always hid under the car**PET E**llie likes playing on.'

Lisa, **Bill**, **Vera**, **Chris**, **Sandra**, **Dan**, **Joe** and **Pete** have all passed their exams.

Page 79

D – UBLIN
E – DINBURGH
I – NNSBRUCK
O – SLO
E – GYPT
J – ERUSALEM
I – STANBUL
R – OME
A – MSTERDAM
R – OTTERDAM
O – TTAWA
N – ICE

They are heading for **Rio de Janeiro**.

Page 80

Bob used Morse code.

B = — • • •

R = • — •

I = • •

T = —

N = — •

E = •

Y = — • — —

S = • • •

P = • — — •

E = •

A = • —

R = • — •

S = • • •

'Britney Spears is on board'.

Page 81

Every other letter needs to be separated out, and the second line needs to be reversed, which leaves, '**You have landed on Mars in the year 3529.**'

Page 82

The notes read: '**b – a – d – d – e – e – d – e – d – d – e – a – d – f – e – d**'.

So the message reads, '**Bad deed. Ed dead. Fed (up)**'. (The last three notes are one octave higher than the rest of the message, thereby equaling 'up').

Page 83

The letters are written into the grid from top to bottom, then up again, then down again.

	A	B	C	D	E
1	A	K	L	U	V
2	B	I	J	M	T	W
3	C	H	N	S	X
4	D	G	O	R	Y
5	E	F	P	Q	Z

'**Leave money in park at midnight**'.

Page 84

The vowels are encoded as A–E, the consonants as 1–21, but in reverse order.

A	B	C	D	E	F	G	H	I	J	K	L	M
E	21	20	19	D	18	17	16	C	15	14	13	12

N	O	P	Q	R	S	T	U	V	W	X	Y	Z
11	B	10	9	8	7	6	A	5	4	3	2	1

"**Hungry. Give me bananas**".

Page 85

They have encoded their names. In addition, they are using letters for words, as in U = you and C = see. Any letters they cannot encrypt like this stay in their normal form, but in lower case.

J	U	D	E	M	A	R	I	O	N
1	2	3	4	5	6	7	8	9	0

Marion: "**Jim is mad! Are you for John or Mario?**"

Judy: "**I'm for Jeremy.**"

Marion: "**Dream on!**"

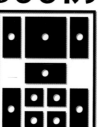

LAGOON BOOKS